Extraordinary Max

Written by Dan & Jen Studt

Illustrated by Kristen Elaine Whalen

© 2022 by Freedom in Christ Ministries

Published by Freedom in Christ Ministries. 9051 Executive Park Dr, Suite 503, Knoxville, TN 37923 • www.ficm.org

ISBN 9780996972574 (pbk)

Written by Dan and Jen Studt • Cover design and Illustrations by Kristen Elaine Whalen • Layout by Courtney Pierce Design
Printed in the United States of America

Hi! I am Max!
I may look like
an ordinary kid,

but something
happened to
me and now...
I am extraordinary!

I knew my sin was keeping me from being close to God, so I asked Jesus to forgive my sins and be my Lord.

Now, because of Jesus, there are new things that are true about me!

I was spiritually dead
because of my sin...

You were dead in
trespasses and sins.
EPHESIANS 2:1

Now I am spiritually alive!

But God, being rich in mercy,
because of the great love with
which He loved us... made us alive
together with Christ.

EPHESIANS 2:4-5

I was an enemy of God...

Once you were enemies...

COLOSSIANS 1:21

Now, I am God's friend!

No longer do I call you servants...
But I have called you friends.

JOHN 15:15

I was in darkness...

For at one time you were darkness...

EPHESIANS 5:8

Now I
live in the
Light!

...but now you are
light in the Lord.
EPHESIANS 5:8

I had a cold heart of stone....

I will remove the heart of stone...

EZEKIEL 36:26

Now I have a tender heart of flesh!

And I will give you a new heart of flesh.

EZEKIEL 36:26

I was a Sinner...

For all have sinned and fall short of the glory of God.

ROMANS 3:23

Loved by God and
called to be Saints...

ROMANS 1:7

Now, I am a Saint!

I was a slave to sin....

Everyone who practices
sin is a slave to sin.

JOHN 8:34

Now, I am free!

We are no longer slaves to sin... We have
been set free from the power of sin.

ROMANS 6:6-7

I may look like an ordinary kid...

But because of Jesus,

I am extraordinary!

Have you ever gotten into trouble? When we disobey, it is called sin. One of the Bible words for sin means 'to miss the mark' like an arrow that misses a target. In this story, Max knew that he had missed the mark and that he was separated from God by his sin.

Every one of us was born separated from God by our sins. This is why Jesus came to earth! Jesus is God's Son. He paid for our sins by dying on the Cross so that we can be forgiven. When we trust Jesus as our Savior, all the changes that happened to Max happen to us.

The good news is that salvation is so much more than getting our sins forgiven so we can go to heaven! Salvation means we go from being separated from God to having life and a relationship with God as Max discovered.

Christians are not extraordinary because of what they do or how hard they try to obey rules. The gospel, or good news, is that Jesus did all the work for our salvation on the cross. When he rose from the dead, he showed proof that He defeated sin, death, and Satan. Jesus said, "I am the resurrection and the life. Whoever believes in me, though he die, yet shall he live... the one who believes will never die. Do you believe this?" (John 11:25-26) If you know you have been separated from God by your sin and want to be forgiven so you can be friends with God, pray this prayer:

Salvation Prayer

Dear Heavenly Father, Thank you for sending your Son, Jesus, to pay for my sin and give me new life. I receive your gift of forgiveness by faith. I trust you and give my life to you as my Lord. Thank you that new things are true about me because you are my Savior. Help me to trust you with everything that happens in my life. In Jesus' name, Amen.

Biblical Rationale for Parents

Are the statements in this book really true? Absolutely, yes.

This book describes what the Bible says is true before and after salvation. There are serious things that are true of someone who does not believe in Jesus. But these are exchanged at the moment of salvation. They are true because of what Jesus has done, and so we receive them by faith. In Jesus, we have a completely new spiritual identity.

Think of it this way... Have you ever burped? Of course, you have! We all do! But, do you go around introducing yourself to people by saying, "Hello, my name is _____ and I'm a burper." No! Of course, you don't. Why not? Because burping is something you do, but it doesn't define who you are. Too often, we hear it said that we are 'Just sinners, saved by grace.' But the New Testament never defines a believer in Christ by their sin.

The Apostle Paul, in Romans 7:20, says, "Now if I do what I do not want, it is no longer I who do it, but sin that dwells within me." See... he says there is a difference between 'me' and the sin that dwells, or lives, in me. Sin lives in our flesh and is destructive, but it no longer defines us. The new things that make you and me and Max extraordinary are true because of what Jesus Christ accomplished on the cross through His death and resurrection. Simply put, we go from being Sinners with a capital 'S' to sinners with a lower case 's.' We are now identified as Saints, "holy ones," because of Jesus.

Is it prideful to believe these things? No, since it's all because of Jesus. That's why we receive it by faith. But not believing these things will cause us to feel defeated or try to rely on our own performance to be accepted by God.

So, when you feel like you don't measure up, remind yourself of the truth of who you are as a new creation in Christ because of the finished work of Jesus: I am spiritually alive (Ephesians 2:5)! I am a friend of Jesus (John 15:15)! I live in the light (Ephesians 5:8)! I have a tender heart of flesh (Ezekiel 36:26)! I am a saint (Romans 1:7)! I am no longer a slave to sin... I'm free (Romans 6:11, 14)! Choose to believe these by faith and then rely on the Holy Spirit to help you live out the change Jesus made in you!

In Christ:

I am accepted...

I am God's child (John 1:12).

I am Jesus' friend (John 15:15).

I have been chosen by God (Ephesians 1:4).

I am forgiven of all my sins (Colossians 1:14).

I am complete in Christ (Colossians 2:10).

I am a Saint (Ephesians 1:1).

I can go straight to Jesus for help (Hebrews 4:14-16).

I am secure...

I belong to God (1 Corinthians 6:19-20).

I cannot be separated from God's love (Romans 8:38-39).

I know God is always working for my good (Romans 8:28-29).

I am free from any blame against me (Romans 8:1).

I don't need to fear because Jesus gives me power, love, and self control (2 Timothy 1:7).

I am safe with Jesus (Colossians 3:1-4).

I am significant...

I am connected to Jesus (John 15:5).

I am a part of God's plan (John 15:16).

I am God's work of art (Ephesians 2:10).

I am God's temple—God lives in me! (1 Corinthians 3:16).

I can always go to God no matter what happens (Ephesians 3:12).

I can do hard things because Jesus helps me (Philippians 4:13).

I am a messenger of God's good news (2 Corinthians 5:17-21).

And there is MORE!

I am _____.
These things are true of me because
I have trusted in Jesus!

Beloved... Colossians 3:12

The Lord's Delight... Psalm 147:11

Beautiful... Psalm 149:4

Unashamed... Romans 10:11

Chosen... Ephesians 1:4

Known... Psalm 139:1

Clean... John 15:3

Treasured... Deuteronomy 7:6

Presentable... Hebrews 10:22

Pure... 1 Corinthians 6:11

Protected... Psalm 91:4

Precious... Isaiah 43:4

Planned... Ephesians 1:11-12

Safe... 1 John 5:18

Gifted... 2 Timothy 1:6

Loved... 1 John 4:10

Provided For... 1 Timothy 6:17

Holy... Hebrews 10:10

Your Child... Romans 8:15

Forgiven... Psalm 103:3

Your Friend... John 15:15

Adopted... Ephesians 1:5

Welcomed... Ephesians 3:12

God's Work of Art... Ephesians. 2:10

An Heir... Romans 8:17

Complete... Colossians 2:10

Free from Condemnation... Romans 8:1

Endnotes

All material is from Freedom in Christ Ministries. For more children's resources and parenting material, go to www.ficm.org/children. For Freedom in Christ books and resources for the whole family, check out our online bookstore: www.freedominchrist.com.

Watch for our next book
Amazing Maisey coming soon!

Amazing Maisey teaches kids how we are adopted by our Father God through faith in Jesus.

OTHER FREEDOM IN CHRIST CHILDREN'S RESOURCES:

The Lightbringers is a resource developed by Freedom in Christ International. It is designed to equip children ages 5 to 11 years old to become fruitful disciples who stay connected to Jesus into their adult lives. It consists of ten action-packed sessions plus specially written versions of *The Steps to Freedom in Christ* for kids. There are 2 editions: the Church Edition and the Family Edition. We encourage you to check it out online to see if it will work for your kids or your children's ministry.

🔥 FREEDOM IN CHRIST

9051 Executive Park Drive, Suite 503, Knoxville, TN 37923 • 865-342-4000 • www.ficm.org.

CPSIA information can be obtained
at www.ICGtesting.com
Printed in the USA
JSHW051925160423
40344JS00002B/3